Principal Cello

Grades 6–8

12 pieces for cello and piano

Selected and edited by
Tim Wells and Alison Moncrieff-Kelly

ABRSM

Contents

A note from the editors

These 12 wonderful pieces cover a wide variety of styles, but they all serve the same purpose: they give recital cellists and their pianists repertoire which is captivating, at times surprising, and always delightful to listen to. As selectors, we had dozens of pieces from which to choose, and we found it rewarding to winnow that list down to such a satisfying group of 12, arranged in this volume roughly in order of difficulty. In particular, it was a delight to rescue some of the pieces from the obscurity into which they had fallen, either through going out of print, or because fashions or tastes had changed.

In editing the cello part, we have tried to give just the right amount of bowing and fingering: enough that every passage is technically clear while still allowing cellists room to make their own expressive decisions.

We hope you enjoy playing these pieces as much as we do!

Tim Wells and Alison Moncrieff-Kelly
May 2015

First published in 2015 by ABRSM (Publishing) Ltd, a wholly owned subsidiary of ABRSM

Reprinted in 2016, 2017

© 2015 by The Associated Board of the Royal Schools of Music
ISBN 978 1 84849 746 7
AB 3789

Music origination by Tim Wells and Jeremy Hughes
Cover design by www.adamhaystudio.com
Printed in England by Halstan & Co. Ltd, Amersham, Bucks.,
on materials from sustainable sources

Intermezzo
EG 115

Edvard Grieg
(1843–1907)

Mélodie arabe

No. 5 from *Cinq romances*, Op. 4

Arranged by Tim Wells
and Alison Moncrieff-Kelly

Aleksandr Glazunov
(1865–1936)

Les cloches

No. 2 from *Deux romances*

Transcribed by Ferdinando Ronchini

Claude Debussy
(1862–1918)

for D. L.

Dance Caprice

Christopher Bunting
(1924–2005)

AB 3789

Chanson triste

No. 3 from *Trois morceaux*, Op. 4

Henryk Pachulski
(1859–1921)

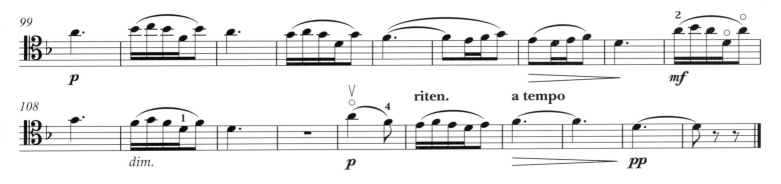

Titania

No. 1 from *The Fairy Ring*

Frederic Austin
(1872–1952)

Gavotte humoristique

Op. 6

William H. Squire
(1871–1963)

* The slurs in bars 13–14 and 17–19, and those in the parallel passage from bar 76, may be omitted.

* The lower note may be omitted.

Allegro
Third movement from *Pohádka* (A Tale)

Leoš Janáček
(1854–1928)

Adoration

Arranged by Tim Wells

Felix Borowski
(1872–1956)

Tzig-Tzig
Danse magyare (Hungarian Dance)

William H. Squire
(1871–1963)

Alla Pollacca

No. 4 from *Quatre morceaux caractéristiques*, Op. 48

Georg Goltermann
(1824–1898)

* The slurs in bars 100 and 102 may be omitted.

Rigaudon

Margaret Hubicki
(1915–2006)